Instructor's
Guide and Answer Key
For Use With

Exploring drafting

by
JOHN R. WALKER

South Holland, Illinois
THE GOODHEART-WILLCOX CO., Inc.
Publishers

Exploring drafting

EXPLORING DRAFTING provides a background in basic drafting. It attempts to make drafting meaningful and interesting.

To The Instructor

In addition to the conventional drafting problems, you will find many other problems that are unique. Also, the range of problem difficulty is such that students with differing abilities will be challenged.

The TEST YOUR KNOWLEDGE questions at the end of each Unit will enable you and the student to check the student's comprehension of the text material.

Problems in OUTSIDE ACTIVITIES (it is preferred that students volunteer for these) offer an opportunity to bring many of the latest techniques and materials of industry into the school drafting room where they can be studied first hand.

The ACTIVITIES also provide a unique opportunity for developing student originality and ingenuity. You will be surprised at the accomplishments of many of your students. They are broad enough in scope to take care of student differences and may be used as a full marking period or semester assignment.

Since drafting room time is usually limited, the WORKBOOK designed to supplement the text will enable the student to progress more rapidly as much time consuming repetitive work (borders, title block, etc.) is supplied in printed form.

In teaching SHEET METAL PATTERN DEVELOPMENT, for example, the instructor does not have to wait until each student has drawn the border, title block and needed views to start the class on the solution of the problem (some students will require only a few minutes while others will need considerable time). With the workbook, all students start on the solution of the problem at the same time. Students with ability do not have to "mark time" while the slower students catch up.

Improving Instruction

Only YOU the instructor can determine what material is best suited for YOUR students and how it should be presented. With advanced students you will probably want to cover the material in depth; with others, a few Units with a limited number of drafting problems solved will be a major accomplishment.

No matter what approach you take, an organized drafting room routine should be established.

1. ALWAYS have a lesson plan and follow it. Modify it as needed. A good lesson plan starts with something that is familiar to the student and progresses into new material in short, easily understood steps rather than in lengthy or difficult steps.
2. "Warm up" the student. Tell and show him:
   a. How he can use the information he

learns and the skills he will develop on the job.

b. What he is to learn.

c. What he can do to help himself learn.

d. Explain the "why" as well as the "how."

e. Spell out how he will be evaluated in class.

3. Use training aids. With them you can:

a. Teach more in less time.

b. Hold the student's interest.

c. Help the student to remember longer.

d. Provide a means for accurate learning.

4. Have a good seating arrangement so that ALL students can see and hear.

5. Make your humor effective. Use humor that will:

a. Make the lesson interesting.

b. Put over an idea.

c. "Break the ice."

6. Remember, there are many types of individuals. Each must be handled in a different manner.

7. Quickly learn your students' names. They feel more important if you call them by name.

8. Give your students credit for good work:

a. Point out work well done.

b. Praise them for honest effort.

c. Let them know you are interested in their progress.

d. Accompany reprimands with praise for work that is well done.

Audio-Visual Aids

Many types of aids are available commercially. Use only those that fit into your program. Do not overlook the advantages of preparing your own. Let your students help.

Investigate the possibility of developing a "teaching kit." This should include a collection of aids and materials (transparencies, slides, tapes, industrial examples, etc.) on a specific unit. The unit should be contained in a specially designed box so it will be readily available to the teacher and student.

Field Trips

Field trips are frequently overlooked in the area of drafting. Much can be learned, and considerable enthusiasm generated through well planned field trips.

One such trip would be a visit to the Industrial Arts and/or Vocational-Technical facilities in your school. This would be an excellent way to show your students how drafting is used in other areas of endeavor.

Do not forget to brief your students before any field trip so that they will know what to look for and can better understand what they will see.

A follow-up evaluation and discussion is a must after a field trip. Often a short theme on what was observed will be helpful.

Mass-Production Problem

There are several problems described in the text that are adaptable to a mass-production project in the drafting room. The problem can be accomplished by a group of students or the entire class can participate in the project. Properly planned, such a project will provide an interesting and challenging experience.

Student Personnel Organization

Involving your students in the management of the drafting room will not only be of value in their development but will free you of many routine duties and allow you more time for instructional purposes.

Establish the duties, using care not to include tasks that are "busy work" or impractical. Prepare a formal job description of each task and provide time for the class to study and discuss the job descriptions. Change them when new and better ways are developed to do the job.

Assign students to the various positions on a rotating basis that will permit each member an equal opportunity to serve.

Test Your Knowledge

At the end of each Unit are questions designed to test the students' comprehension and coverage of the material. Answers to these questions will be found on the following pages. When questions require rather extensive answers, reference is given to a specific page or figure where the answer will be found.

UNIT 1 (Page 10)
1. See page 7
2. b
3. d
4. Architects, engineers, designers, map makers, etc.
5. Aerospace, structural drafting, architecture, electronic and electrical drafting, engineering graphics, technical drawing, topographical drafting.

UNIT 2 (Page 28)
1. short strokes
2. border line
3. enlarged, reduced
4. See page 18
5. dimension
6. left to right, top down
7. arrowheads

UNIT 3 (Page 43)
1. smooth, flat surface needed for drafting
2. b
3. draw horizontal lines
4. triangles
5. circles and arcs
6. sandpaper pad, pencil pointer
7. see page 39
8. tape, thumb tack, staple (tape)
9. protractor
10. 4H-5H
11. H-2H
12. Almost every line on the drawing must be a measured length
13. See Fig. 3-24, page 42

UNIT 4 (Page 57)
1. a. construction or guide line

b. border line
c. visible line
d. dimension line
e. hidden line
f. center line
g. cutting plane line
h. section lines
i. phantom line
2. line conventions
3. almost every line on a mechanical drawing must be a measured length.
4. a. device used to measure
b. size to which an object is to be drawn
5. See Fig. 4-5, page 47
6. architect's, engineer's and mechanical draftsmen's
7. T-square
8. triangles
9. erasing shield
10. compass
11. tape, thumb tack, staple
12. tape

UNIT 5 - No Questions

UNIT 6 (Page 88)
1. See page 83
2. it can be drawn rapidly and is highly legible
3. vertical or inclined
4. H - 2H
5. keep letter height uniform
6. Braddock-Rowe Lettering Triangle, Ames Lettering Instrument, special typewriter, mechanical lettering devices
7. See page 87

UNIT 7 (Page 99)
1. Instruments
2. Multiview drawing
3. a. top view
b. front view
c. right side view
d. left side view
e. back view
f. bottom view
4. orthographic projection
5. front, top, right side view

Answer Key

UNIT 8 (Page 113)
1. See page 107
2. sizes of the geometric features of an object.
3. additional information along with size
4. bottom of the sheet
5. bottom and right side of sheet
6. b
7. arrowheads
8. the true shape of the object
9. grouped together, scattered
10. c
11. inch symbol (")
12. center

UNIT 9 (Page 125)
1. See page 119
2. sectional views are necessary for a clear understanding of the shape of complicated parts.
3. cutting plane line
4. letters - A-A, B-B, etc.
5. full section
6. half section
7. revolved section
8. a small portion of a sectional view will provide the required information
9. conventional break
10. section lining

UNIT 10 (Page 133)
1. See page 130
2. Must be evaluated individually
3. line, 90 degrees
4. front auxiliary
5. only half of the view

UNIT 11 (Page 146)
1. b
2. See page 137
3. isometric, cavalier oblique, cabinet oblique, general oblique, parallel (one point) perspective, angular (two point) perspective
4. See Fig. 11-4, page 138
5. non-isometric lines
6. See Fig. 11-10, page 141
7. 15 degrees, 30 degrees, 45 degrees
8. See page 144

UNIT 12 (Page 153)
1. See page 150
2. a. surface development
   b. sheet metal drafting
3. stretchouts
4. hobbies, clothing, footwear, aerospace parts, heating and air conditioning ducts and pipes, appliances, wallets, handbags, etc.
5. a sharp fold or bend must be made on the line
6. there is a curved surface
7. See Fig. 12-4, page 152
8. French Curve

UNIT 13 (Page 169)
1. See page 165
2. detail
3. assembly
4. subassembly
5. c
6. d
7. a
8. b
9. e

UNIT 14 (Page 181)
1. See page 177
2. white lines on a blue background
3. See page 177
4. dry
5. with ammonia vapors
6. photographically
7. blow backs
8. tracing cloth, film, paper
9. sharp, dense
10. India
11. ink running under the T-square or angle

UNIT 15 (Page 189)
1. See page 183
2. graphic picture showing a portion of the earth's surface
3. surveyor
4. too large
5. a town lot
6. street and lot layouts
7. physical features of land
8. See Fig. 15-8, page 188

UNIT 16 (Page 196)
1. See page 191
2. line graph, bar graph, circle graph
3. line graph, a curve
4. shows what each curve represents
5. evaluate individually
6. circle or pie graph
7. evaluate individually
8. brightens your presentation and makes the information stand out

UNIT 17 (Page 210)
1. See page 199
2. See page 201
3. See page 204
4. See page 199
5. drilling, reaming, countersinking, tapping, etc.
6. milling machine, shaper, planer, broach, surface grinder
7. See Fig. 17-20, page 206
8. pattern
9. shrinks slightly when it cools
10. not as smooth or as accurate, die casting
11. See Fig. 17-24, page 207

UNIT 18 (Page 214)
1. by electricity (arc welding), burning gases (usually oxyacetylene)
2. d
3. See Fig. 18-4, page 212
4. See Fig. 18-5, page 213
5. See Fig. 18-6, page 214
6. See Fig. 18-7, page 215
7. welds not made in the shop
8. because the individual pieces are seldom cut to size, welded and machined in the same general area

UNIT 19 (Page 226)
1. Evaluate individually
2. a device used to hold two objects or parts together
3. See page 219
4. make adjustments, transmit motion, assemble parts, apply pressure, make measurements
5. See Fig. 19-3, page 220
6. See Fig. 19-4, page 220
7. See Fig. 19-5, page 221

8. wood screws and nails
9. E, G, F, D, A, B, C

UNIT 20 (Page 234)
1. See page 231
2. easier and quicker to draw
3. See Fig. 20-4, page 231
4. See page 232
5. components are drawn in pictorial form and are shown in their proper location. See Fig. 20-8, page 233
6. visible object line
7. connection or wiring diagrams

UNIT 21 (Page 252)
1. See page 236
2. carpenters, masons, plumbers, electricians, roofers, lumber yard workers, etc.
3. See page 237
4. 1/4" = 1'-0"
5. plot plan
6. elevations
7. d
8. sectional views
9. See Fig. 21-15, page 248

UNIT 22 (Page 262)
1. written or drawn
2. true
3. symbols, see page 257
4. light pen, alphabet numbers and letters, key board with push buttons
5. cathode ray
6. pictures

UNIT 23 (Page 272)
1. See page 265
2. a scale replica of a planned or existing object
3. a full size 3-dimensional copy of an object.
4. a full size operating model of the production item
5. Evaluate individually
6. balsa
7. sandpaper
8. See page 272

UNIT 24 (Page 281)
1. See page 275

2. d
3. a. B
   b. D
   c. E
   d. A
   e. C
   f. F
   g. G

UNIT 25 (Page 285)
1. Evaluate individually
2. Evaluate individually
3. function, honesty, appearance, crafts-manship
4. Evaluate individually

UNIT 26 (Page 290)
1. working plans and detailed drawing
2. trainee draftsman, junior draftsman, draftsman
3. neat, accurate and is able to draw rapidly
4. simplify and improve the operation and appearance of industrial products
5. teaching
6. architects, licensed
7. aeronautical, industrial, chemical, structural, civil, electrical, etc.
8. models, mockups and prototypes of a product, what it will look like and, in some cases, how it will work
9. technical illustrator